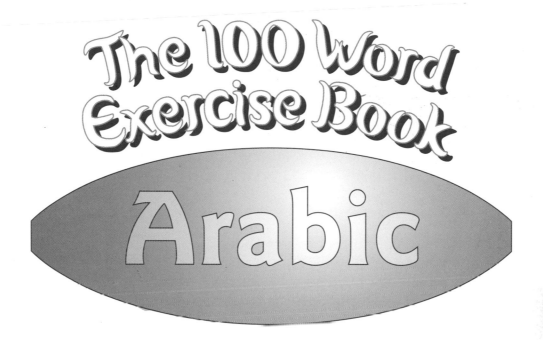

The 100 Word Exercise Book

Arabic

Series concept: Jane Wightwick

Arabic edition: Mahmoud Gaafar

GW

Published by *GW Publishing*
47a High Street
Chinnor
Oxfordshire OX9 4DJ

First published 1999

© *GW Publishing 1999*

ISBN 1-903103-00-2

Designed by: Robert Bowers

Illustrated by: Mahmoud Gaafar

Printed in Hong Kong
by Wing King Tong

◎ CONTENTS

◎ INTRODUCTION

In this activity book you'll find 100 key words for you to learn to read in Arabic. All of the activities are designed specifically for reading non-Latin script languages. Many of the activities are inspired by the kind of games used to teach children to read their own language: flashcards, matching games, memory games, joining exercises, etc. This is not only a more effective method of learning to read a new script, but also much more fun.

We've included a **Scriptbreaker** to get you started. This is a friendly introduction to the Arabic script that will give you tips on how to remember the letters.

Then you can move on to the eight **Topics**. Each topic presents essential words in large type. There is also a pronunciation guide so you know how to say the words. These words are also featured in the tear-out **Flashcard** section at the back of the book. When you've mastered the words, you can go on to try out the activities and games for that topic.

There's also a **Round-up** section to review all your new words and the **Answers** to all the activities to check yourself.

Follow this 4-step plan for maximum success:

1 Have a look at the key topic words with their pictures. Then tear out the flashcards and shuffle them. Put them Arabic side up. Try to remember what the word means and turn the card over to check with the English. When you can do this, cover the pronunciation and try to say the word and remember the meaning by looking at the Arabic script only.

2 Put the cards English side up and try to say the Arabic word. Try the cards again each day both ways around. (When you can remember a card for seven days in a row, you can file it.)

3 Try out the activities and games for each topic. This will re-inforce your recognition of the key words.

4 After you have covered all the topics, you can try the activities in the **Round-up** section to test your knowledge of all the 100 words in the book. You can also try shuffling all the flashcards together to see how many you can remember.

This flexible and fun way of reading your first words in Arabic should give you a head start whether you're learning at home or in a group.

◎ SCRIPTBREAKER

The purpose of this Scriptbreaker is to introduce you to the Arabic script and how it is formed. You should not try to memorize the alphabet at this stage, nor try to write the letters yourself. Instead, have a quick look through this section and then move on to the topics, glancing back if you want to work out the letters in a particular word. Remember, though, that recognizing the whole shape of the word in an unfamiliar script is just as important as knowing how it is made up. Using this method you will have a much more instinctive recall of vocabulary and will gain the confidence to expand your knowledge in other directions.

The Arabic script is not nearly as difficult as it might seem at first glance. There are 28 letters (only two more than in the English alphabet), no capital letters, and, unlike English, words are spelled as they sound. There are two main points to etch into your brain:

- Arabic is written from right to left.
- The letters are "joined up" — you cannot "print" a word as you can in English.

◎ The alphabet

The easiest way of tackling the alphabet is to divide it into similarly shaped letters. For example, here are two groups of similar letters. The only difference between them is the dots:

ح (the letter *наa*)   ب (the letter *baa*)

ج (the letter *jeem*)   ت (the letter *taa*)

خ (the letter *khaa*)   ث (the letter *thaa*)

When these letters join to other letters they change their shape. The most common change is that they lose their "tails":

$$\text{تج} = \text{ج} + \text{ت} \qquad \text{حب} = \text{ب} + \text{ح} \ \text{(read from } right\ to\ left)$$

Because letters change their shape like this, they have an *initial*, a *medial* (middle) and a *final* form. For example, the letter ج (*jeem*) changes like this:

at the beginning of a word (*initial*)   جـ...

in the middle of a word (*medial*)   ...ـجـ...

at the end of a word (*final*)   ...ـج

- ✔ Arabic has 28 letters and no capital letters
- ✔ Arabic reads right to left
- ✔ Arabic is written in "joined up" writing
- ✔ The "tail" is generally chopped off before joining to the next letter

A few letters change their shapes completely depending on where they fall in a word. For example, the letter ھ (*haa*) changes like this:

initial	ـهـ...
medial	...ـهـ...
final	ـه...

In addition, there are six letters which *never* join to the letter *following* (to their left) and so hardly change shape at all. These are:

و (*waw*)   ا (*alif*)

د (*daal*)   ذ (*THaal*)

ر (*raa*)   ز (*zay*)

You will find more details of how the individual letters change their shape in the table on page 8.

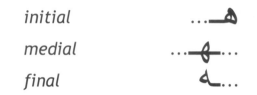 Formation of words

We can use the principles of joining letters to form words.

So, for example, the Arabic word for "river" (*nahr*) is written like this:

(*nahr*) نـهر = (r) ر + (h) ھ + (n) ن   ←

The Arabic word for "belt" (*Hizaam*), contains two non-joining letters and is written like this:

(*Hizaam*) حزام = (m) م + (aa) ا + (z) ز + (H) ح   ←

You may have noticed that some of the vowels seem to be missing from the script. In written Arabic, the three short vowels (*a, i, u*) are not written as part of the script but as vowel signs above or below the letter. The short *a* is written as a dash above the letter (ـَ); the short *i* as a dash below (ـِ); and the short *u* as a comma-shape above (ـُ). This is similar to English shorthand, where we might write "bnk" instead of "bank". Here are the words for "river" and "belt" again, this time with the vowel signs:

نَهر (*nahr*)   حِزام (*Hizaam*)

In this book we have included these vowel signs in the topics, but dropped them in the review section (*Round-up*). Most material for native speakers will leave them out as you are presumed to know them. This makes it all the more important for you to start recognizing a word without the short vowels.

- ✔ Arabic letters have an *initial*, *medial* ("middle") and *final* form, depending on their position in the word
- ✔ Many Arabic letters simply lose their tails for the *medial* and *final* form
- ✔ A few letters change their shape completely
- ✔ 6 letters don't join to the letter after and hardly change at all
- ✔ The short vowels (*a, i, u*) are written as vowel signs above and below the letter and are not usually included in modern written Arabic

◎ Pronunciation tips

This activity book has simplified some aspects of pronunciation in order to emphasize the basics. Don't worry at this stage about being precisely correct – the other letters in a word will help you to be understood. Many Arabic letters are pronounced in a similar way to their English equivalents, but here are a few that need special attention:

ص (*saad*)	a strong "s", pronounced with the tongue on the roof of the mouth rather than up against the teeth
ض (*Daad*)	a strong "d", pronounced with the tongue on the roof of the mouth rather than up against the teeth

ط (Taa)	a strong "t", pronounced with the tongue on the roof of the mouth rather than up against the teeth
ظ (zaa)	a strong "z", pronounced with the tongue on the roof of the mouth rather than up against the teeth
ح (Haa)	pronounced as a breathy "h"
خ (khaa)	pronounced like the "ch" in the Scottish "loch"
ع ('ayn)	the sound most often associated with Arabic, and most difficult to produce: a sort of guttural "ah"-sound
غ (ghayn)	pronounced like the French throaty "r" as in "rue"
ء (hamza)	a strange "half letter". Not really pronounced at all, but has the effect of cutting short the previous letter
ة (taa marboota)	a version of ت (taa) that only appears at the end of words and is pronounced "a"

Summary of the Arabic alphabet

The table below shows all the Arabic letters in the three positions, with the Arabic letter name, followed by the sound. Remember that this is just for reference and you shouldn't expect to take it all in at once. If you know the basic principles of how the Arabic script works, you will slowly come to recognize the individual letters.

	initial:	medial:	final:		initial:	medial:	final:		initial:	medial:	final:
alif[1] a/u/i/aa	ا	ـا	ـا	zaa z	ز	ـز	ـز	qaaf q	ق	ـق	ـق
baa b	بـ	ـبـ	ـب	seen s	سـ	ـسـ	ـس	kaaf k	كـ	ـكـ	ـك
taa t	تـ	ـتـ	ـت	sheen sh	شـ	ـشـ	ـش	laam[2] l	لـ	ـلـ	ـل
thaa th	ثـ	ـثـ	ـث	Saad S	صـ	ـصـ	ـص	meem m	مـ	ـمـ	ـم
jaa j	جـ	ـجـ	ـج	Daad D	ضـ	ـضـ	ـض	noon n	نـ	ـنـ	ـن
Haa H	حـ	ـحـ	ـح	Taa T	طـ	ـطـ	ـط	haa h	هـ	ـهـ	ـه
khaa kh	خـ	ـخـ	ـخ	Zaa Z	ظـ	ـظـ	ـظ	waaw w/oo	و	ـو	ـو
daal d	د	ـد	ـد	'ayn '	عـ	ـعـ	ـع	yaa y/ee	يـ	ـيـ	ـي
THaal TH	ذ	ـذ	ـذ	ghayn gh	غـ	ـغـ	ـغ				
raa r	ر	ـر	ـر	faa f	فـ	ـفـ	ـف				

(1) When *alif* begins a word it is usually written with a *hamza* sign <u>above</u> (أ) if the word starts with *a* or *u* or <u>below</u> (إ) if the word starts with *i*. A *madda* sign is written above (آ) if the word starts with a long *aa*.

(2) Note the special combination when *alif* is written after *laam*: لا, as in دولاب (*doolaab*, meaning "cupboard").

① AROUND THE HOME

Look at the pictures of things you might find in a house.
Tear out the flashcards for this topic.
Follow steps 1 and 2 of the plan in the introduction.

مائِدة
maa-ida

تِليفزيون
tileefizyoon

شُبّاك
shubbaak

كُرسي
kursee

كُمبيوتر
kumbiyootir

تِليفون
tileefoon

كَنَبة *kanaba*

سَرير
sareer

ثلاّجة
thallaaja

دولاب
doolaab

فُرن *furn*

باب
baab

Match the pictures with the words, as in the example.

كَنَبة
سَرير
شُباك
مائِدة
تِليفِزيون
كُرسي
كُمبيوتر
تِليفون

Now match the Arabic household words to the English.

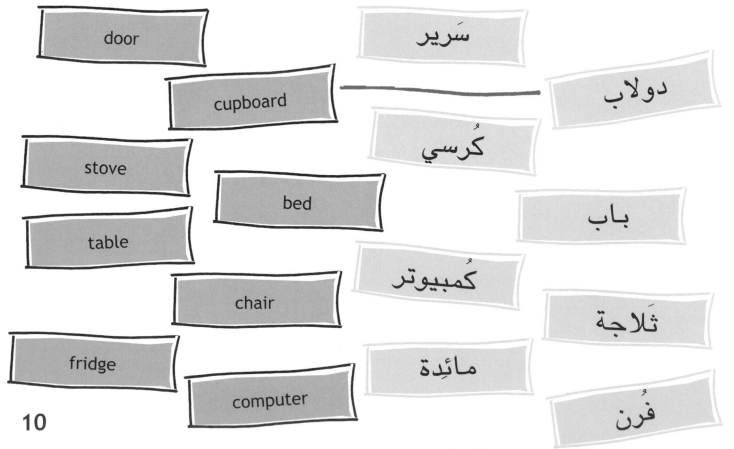

door

cupboard

stove

bed

table

chair

fridge

computer

سَرير

دولاب

كُرسي

باب

كُمبيوتر

ثَلاجة

مائِدة

فُرن

Match the words and their pronunciation.

مائِدة

دولاب

كُمبيوتر

سَرير

شُبّاك

تِليفون

تِليفِزيون

كُرسي

shubbaak

sareer

tileefoon

kursee

tileefizyoon

maa-ida

kumbiyootir

doolaab

See if you can find these words in the word square.
The words run *right to left*.

فُرن

سَرير

كُرسي

ثَلاجة

باب

كَنَبة

ذ	و	ح ت	ر	ي	ر	سـ
ط	ة	لا ج ث	شـ	ا	فـ
د	هـ	ز تـ خ لـ د	ثـ
ة	بـ	ك ن فـ ق	و	ظ
ك	فـ	ي سـ ر ك	يـ	مـ
ن	يـ	ا ج سـ ن	عـ	ط
ع	ن	ر فـ ة ذ	فـ	و
ث	فـ	ة حـ غـ	ب	ا	بـ

11

◎ **D**ecide where the household items should go. Then write the correct number in the picture, as in the example.

10 كُمبيوتر	7 دولاب	4 تِليفزيون	1 مائِدة
11 شُبّاك	8 فُرن	5 تِليفون	2 كُرسي
12 باب	9 ثَلاجة	6 سَرير	3 كَنَبة

Now see if you can fill in the household word at the bottom of the page by choosing the correct Arabic.

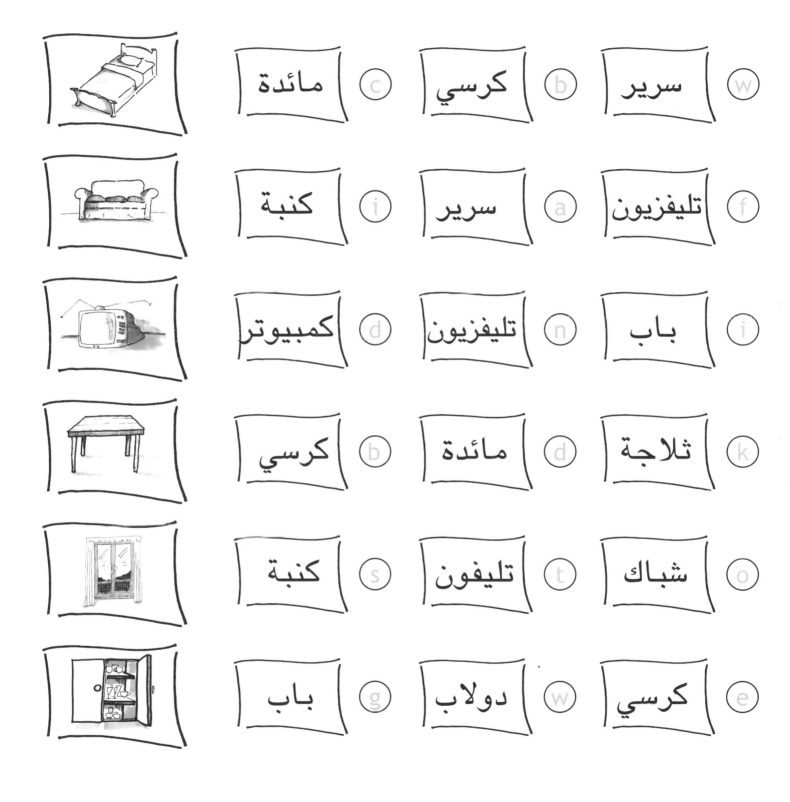

c) مائدة	b) كرسي	w) سرير
i) كنبة	a) سرير	f) تليفزيون
d) كمبيوتر	n) تليفزيون	i) باب
b) كرسي	d) مائدة	k) ثلاجة
s) كنبة	t) تليفون	o) شباك
g) باب	w) دولاب	e) كرسي

English word: (w) ( ) ( ) ( ) ( ) ( )

② CLOTHES

Look at the pictures of different clothes.
Tear out the flashcards for this topic.
Follow steps 1 and 2 of the plan in the introduction.

حِزام
ʜizaam

بُلوفر
buloofir

شورت
shoort

بَنطَلون
banTaloon

جَورَب
jawrab

تي شيرت
tee-sheert

مِعطَف
mi'Taf

جيبة
jeeba

فُستان
fustaan

قُبعَة
qubba'a

حِذاء ʜiTHaa

قَميص qamees

14

◎ **M**atch the Arabic words and their pronunciation.

فُستان

شورت

حِذاء

حِزام

قَميص

تي شيرت

قُبَّعة

جَورَب

fustaan

tee-sheert

shoort

jawrab

qubba'a

qamees

ḥizaam

ḥiṭḥaa

◎ **S**ee if you can find these clothes in the word square.
The words run *right to left*.

ق	ي	ث	ب	ل	و	ف	ر
ج	و	ر	ب	لا	ج	ة	ط
ث	د	خ	ل	ز	ت	ه	د
ظ	و	ق	ف	ج	ي	ب	ه
م	ي	خ	ر	س	ي	ف	ك
ب	ن	ط	ل	و	ن	ي	ظ
و	ف	م	ع	ط	ف	ا	م
ح	ذ	ا	ء	غ	ة	ف	ث

15

Now match the Arabic words, their pronunciation, and the English meaning, as in the example.

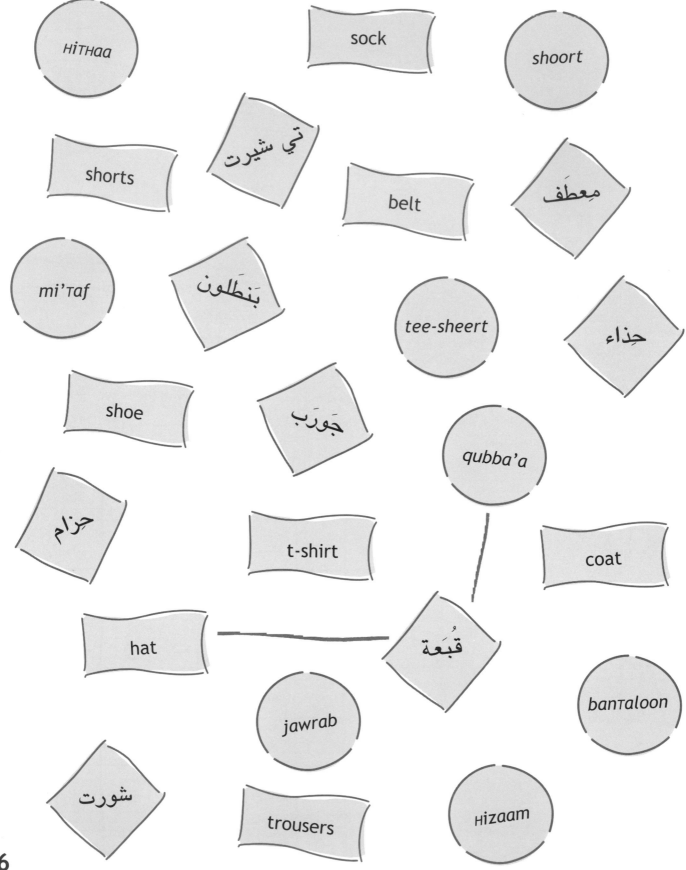

HiтHaa

sock

shoort

تي شيرت

shorts

belt

مِعطَف

mi'тaf

بَنطَلون

tee-sheert

حِذاء

shoe

جَورَب

qubba'a

حزام

t-shirt

coat

hat

قُبَّعة

banтaloon

jawrab

شورت

trousers

Hizaam

16

Candy is going on vacation. Count how many of each type of clothing she is packing in her suitcase.

قبعة	2	معطف	☐	حزام	☐	حذاء	☐
بنطلون	☐	شورت	☐	فستان	☐	جورب	☐
جيبة	☐	تي شيرت	☐	قميص	☐	بلوفر	☐

Someone has ripped up the Arabic words for clothes.
Can you join the two halves of the words, as the example?

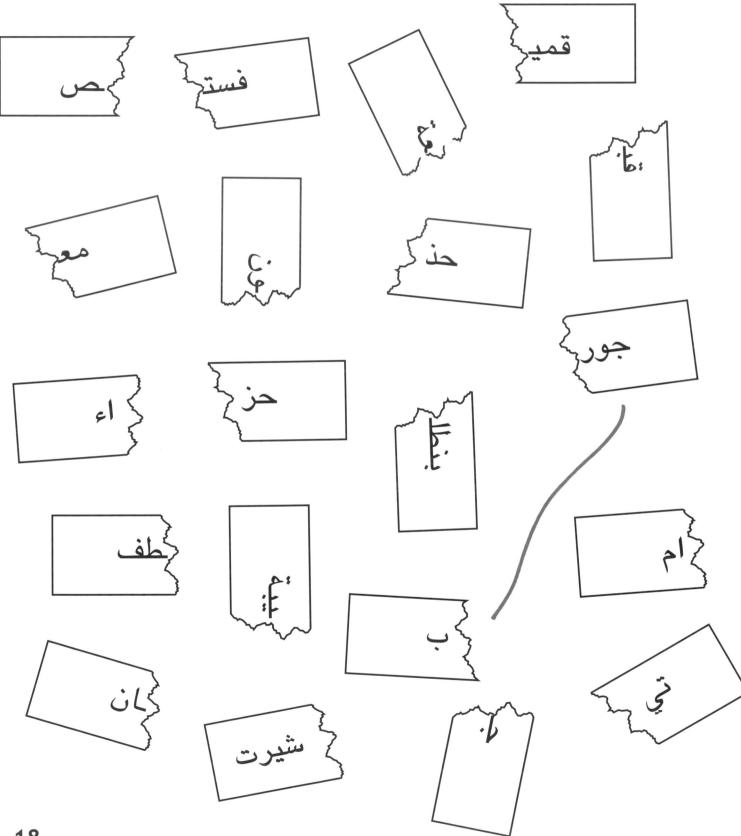

❸ AROUND TOWN

Look at the pictures of things you might find around town.
Tear out the flashcards for this topic.
Follow steps 1 and 2 of the plan in the introduction.

فُندُق
funduq

أُوتوبيس
ootoobees

بَيت
bayt

سَيّارة
sayyaara

سِينما
seenimaa

دَراجة
darraaja

قِطار
qiTaar

تاكسي
taaksee

مَدرَسة *madrasa*

شارِع *shaari'*

مَحَل *maHall*

مَطعَم *maT'am*

○ **M**atch the Arabic words to their English equivalents.

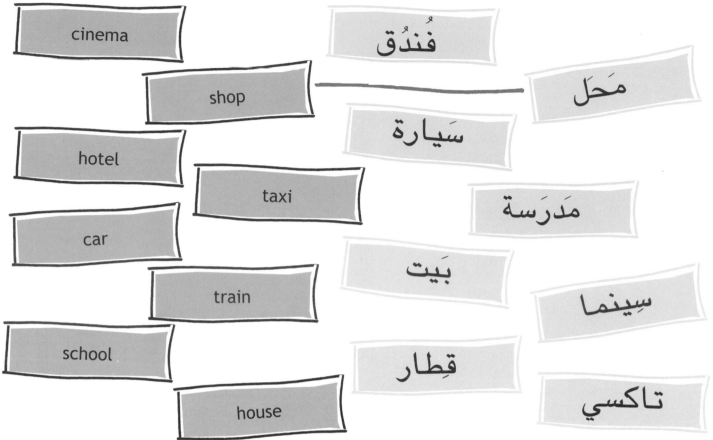

English	Arabic
cinema	فُنْدُق
shop	مَحَل
hotel	سَيّارة
taxi	مَدْرَسة
car	بَيت
train	سِينما
school	قِطار
house	تاكسي

○ **N**ow list the correct order of the English words to match the Arabic word chain, as in the example.

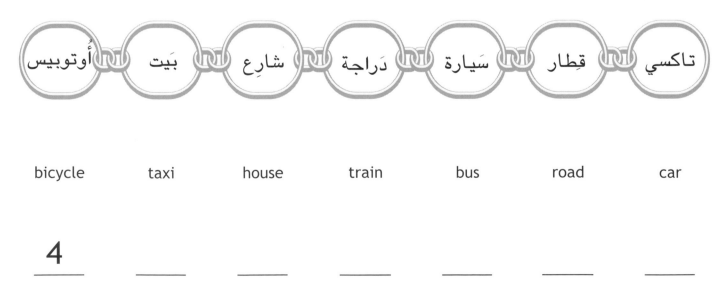

أُوتوبيس ‧ بَيت ‧ شارِع ‧ دَراجة ‧ سَيّارة ‧ قِطار ‧ تاكسي

bicycle   taxi   house   train   bus   road   car

4 ___ ___ ___ ___ ___ ___ ___

◎ **M**atch the words to the signs.

أُوتوبيس	دَراجة	سَيارة	مَدرَسة
تاكسي	فُندُق	قِطار	مَطعَم

Now choose the Arabic word that matches the picture to fill in the English word at the bottom of the page.

English word: ⓢ ◯ ◯ ◯ ◯ ◯

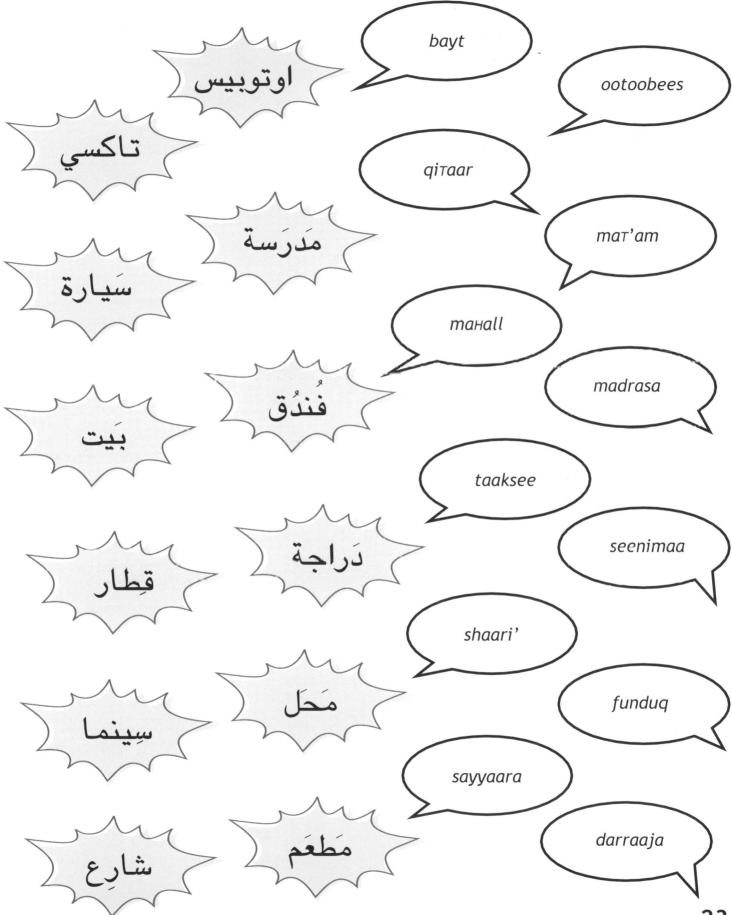

④ COUNTRYSIDE

Look at the pictures of things you might find in the countryside.
Tear out the flashcards for this topic.
Follow steps 1 and 2 of the plan in the introduction.

تَل   tal

جِسر

jisr

مَزرَعة

mazra'a

جَبَل

jabal

بُحيرة

buнayra

شَجَرة

shajara

وَردة

warda

نَهر   nahr

بَحر   baнr

حَقل   наql

صَحراء   saнraa

غابة

ghaaba

24

Can you match all the countryside words to the pictures?

جَبَل

مَزرَعة

بَحر

غابة

صَحراء

تَل

بُحيرة

جِسر

نَهر

وَردة

شَجَرة

حقل

⊚ **N**ow tick (✔) the features you can find in this
landscape.

جِسر ✔	شَجَرة ☐	صَحراء ☐	تَل ☐
جبَل ☐	بَحر ☐	حَقل ☐	غابة ☐
بُحيرة ☐	نَهر ☐	وَردة ☐	مَزرَعة ☐

◎ **M**atch the Arabic words and their pronunciation.

- -

◎ **S**ee if you can find these words in the word square.
The words run *right to left*.

شَجَرة
مَزرَعة
تَل
وَردة
جِسر
بُحيرة

ه	فـ	و	سـ	بـ	ثـ	يـ	نـ
ة	ر	جـ	شـ	بـ	خ	و	جـ
د	هـ	تـ	ة	د	ر	و	ثـ
ة	ر	يـ	حـ	بـ	قـ	و	ظ
ق	يـ	ة	عـ	ر	ز	مـ	ثـ
ف	يـ	نـ	و	بـ	ظ	ل	تـ
م	ا	غ	طـ	قـ	مـ	فـ	و
ب	مـ	سـ	جـ	ا	ذ	ضـ

27

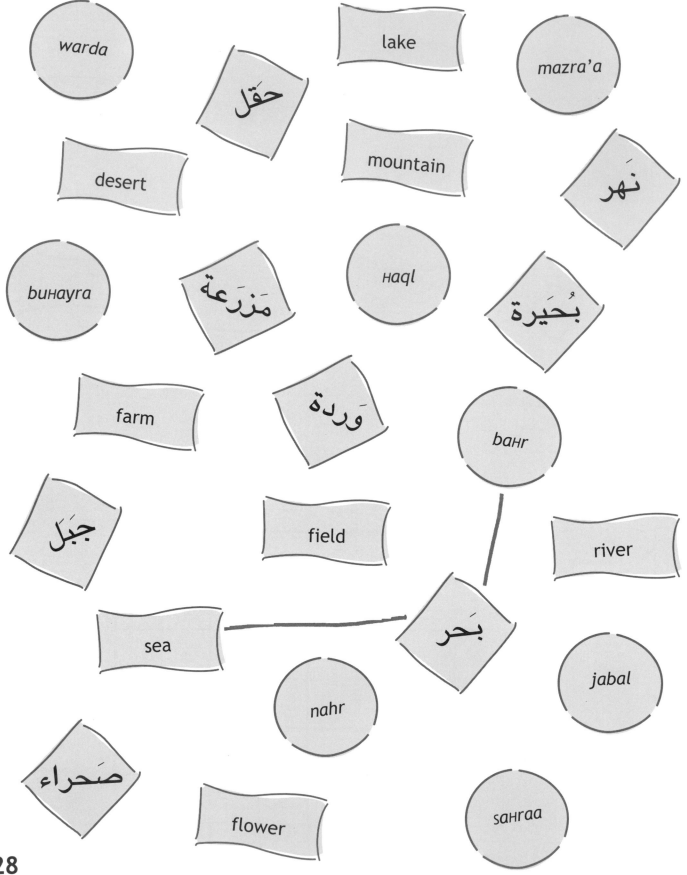

Finally, test yourself by joining the Arabic words, their pronunciation, and the English meanings, as in the example.

warda

lake

mazra'a

حَقل

desert

mountain

نَهر

buнayra

مَزرعة

нaql

بُحَيرة

farm

وَردة

baнr

جبَل

field

river

sea

بَحر

jabal

nahr

صَحراء

flower

saнraa

28

⑤ OPPOSITES

Look at the pictures.
Tear out the flashcards for this topic.
Follow steps 1 and 2 of the plan in the introduction.

وَسِخ
wasikh

نَظيف
nazeef

صَغير
sagheer

كَبير
kabeer

رَخيص
rakhees

خَفيف
khafeef

بَطيء
baтee

غالٍ
ghaalee

ثَقيل
thaqeel

سَريع
saree'

قَديم
qadeem

جَديد
jadeed

29

Join the Arabic words to their English equivalents.

English	Arabic
expensive	نَظيف
big	ثَقيل
light	صَغير
slow	قَديم
clean	جَديد
inexpensive ————	رَخيص
dirty	سَريع
small	بَطيء
heavy	غالٍ
new	وَسِخ
fast	خَفيف
old	كَبير

Now choose the Arabic word that matches the picture to fill in the English word at the bottom of the page.

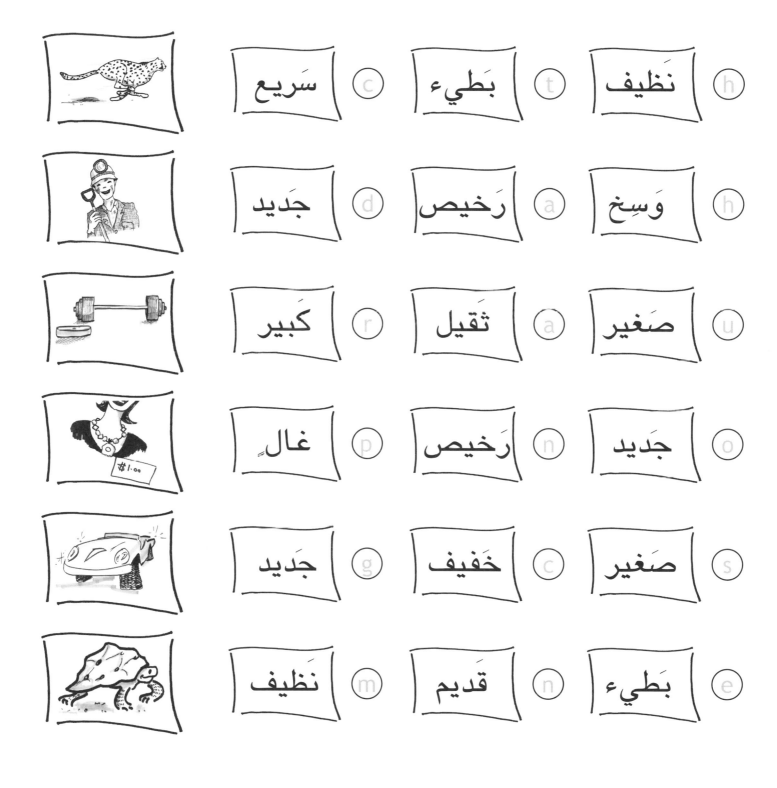

h	نَظيف	t	بَطيء	c	سَريع
h	وَسِخ	a	رَخيص	d	جَديد
u	صَغير	a	ثَقيل	r	كَبير
o	جَديد	n	رَخيص	p	غالٍ
s	صَغير	c	خَفيف	g	جَديد
e	بَطيء	n	قَديم	m	نَظيف

English word: ◯ ◯ ◯ ◯ ◯ ◯

Find the odd one out in these groups of words.

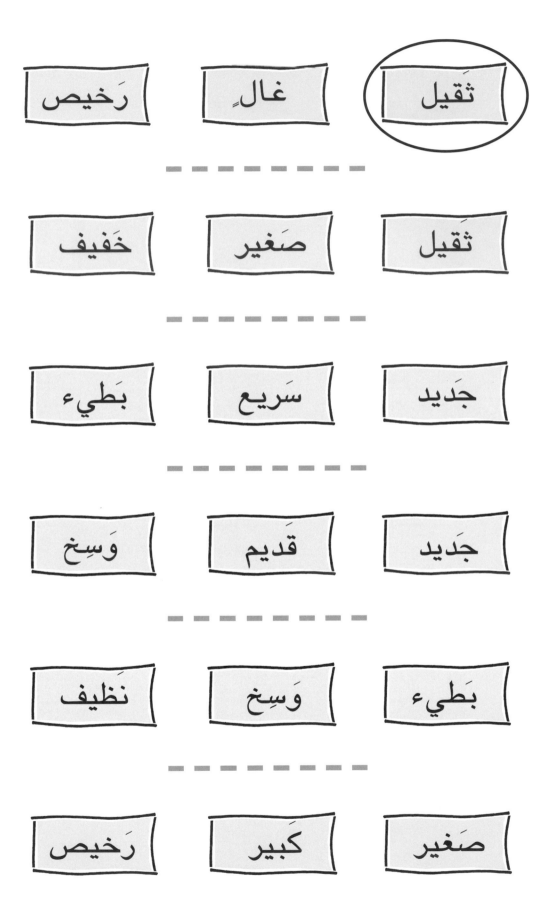

رَخيص غالٍ ثَقيل

خَفيف صَغير ثَقيل

بَطيء سَريع جَديد

وَسِخ قَديم جَديد

نَظيف وَسِخ بَطيء

رَخيص كَبير صَغير

32

Finally, join the English words to their Arabic opposites, as in the example.

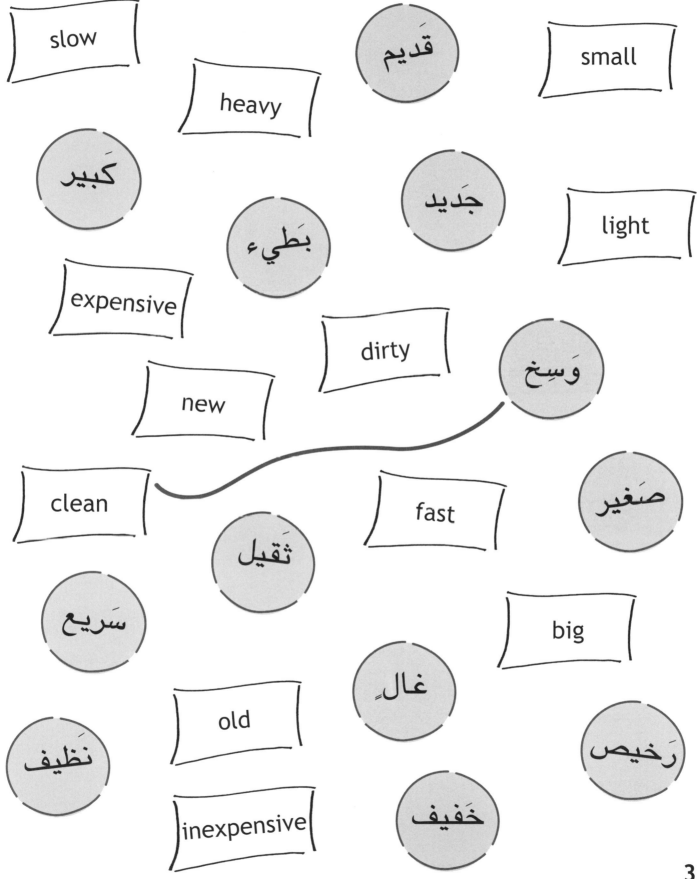

slow

heavy

قَديم

small

كَبير

بَطيء

جَديد

light

expensive

dirty

وَسِخ

new

clean

fast

صَغير

ثَقيل

سَريع

big

غالٍ

old

نَظيف

رَخيص

خَفيف

inexpensive

6 ANIMALS

Look at the pictures.
Tear out the flashcards for this topic.
Follow steps 1 and 2 of the plan in the introduction.

بَطة
baṭṭa

فيل
feel

قِطة
qiṭṭa

كَلب
kalb

أرنَب
arnab

قِرد
qird

سَمَكة
samaka

خَروف *kharoof*

فأر *faar*

بقَرة
baqara

حُصان *Husaan*

أسَد *asad*

34

Match the animals to their associated pictures, as in the example.

أرنَب

حُصان

قِطة

قِرد

كَلب

خَروف

فَأر

أسَد

سَمَكة

بَقَرة

Now match the Arabic to the pronunciation.

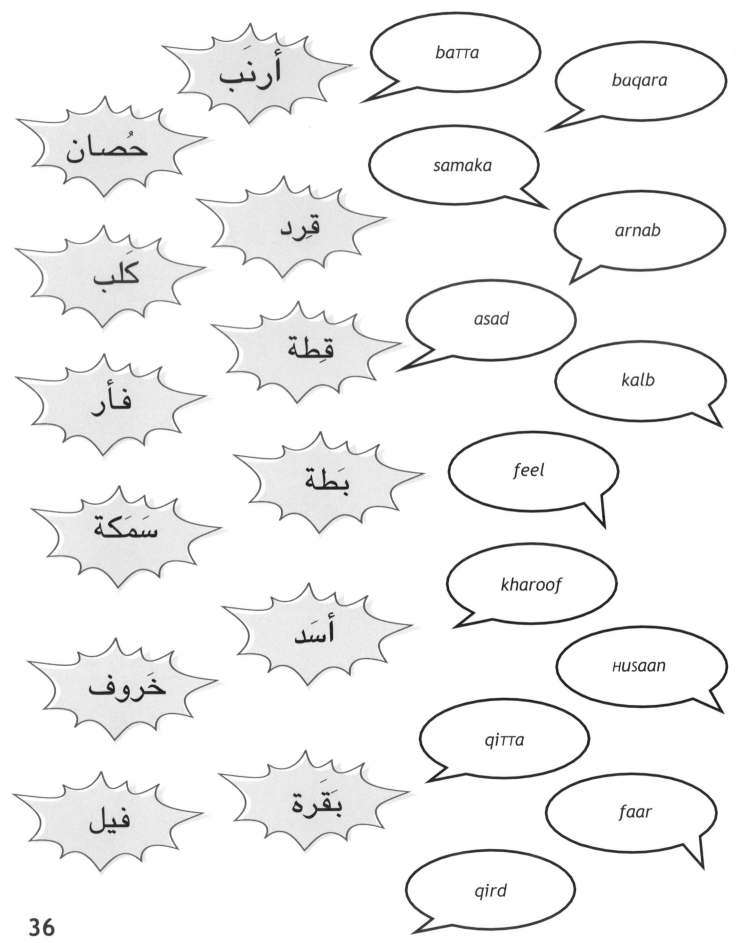

Tick (✔) the animal words you can find in the word pile.

بُحَيرة   قِطة   كُرسي   سَيارة

أرنَب   فيل   خَروف   سَرير

ثَقيل   كَنَبة   سينما   حِذاء

تَل   أسَد   بقَرة   سَمكة

37

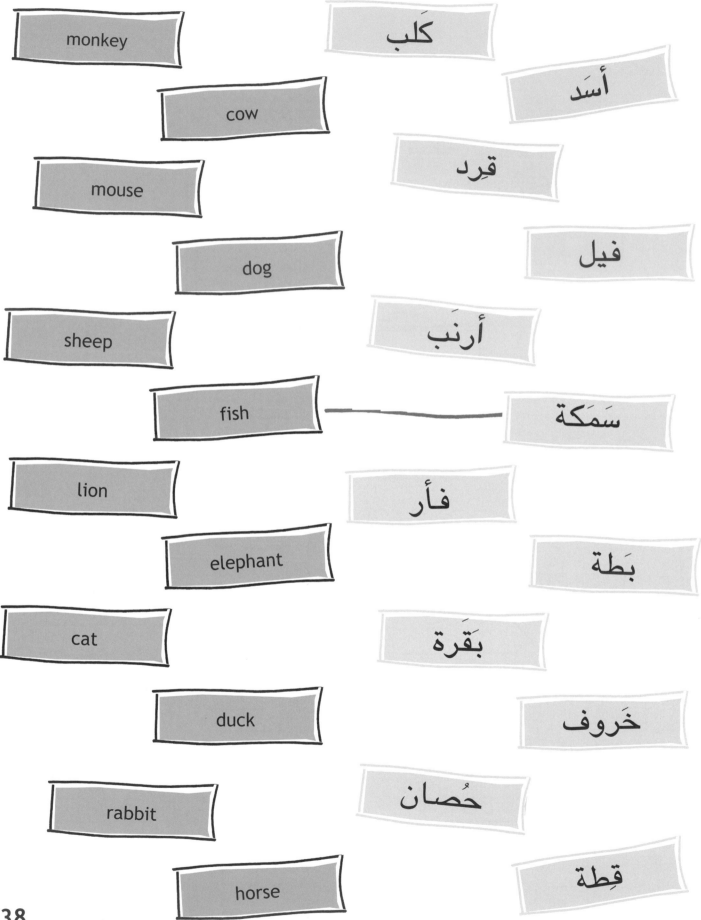

Join the Arabic animals to their English equivalents.

monkey

كَلب

أَسَد

cow

قِرد

mouse

فيل

dog

أَرنَب

sheep

fish ———— سَمَكة

lion

فأر

elephant

بَطة

cat

بَقَرة

duck

خَروف

rabbit

حُصان

horse

قِطة

38

⑦ PARTS OF THE BODY

Look at the pictures of parts of the body.
Tear out the flashcards for this topic.
Follow steps 1 and 2 of the plan in the introduction.

إصبَع
isba'

رَأس
ra-as

ذِراع
THI*raa*

عَين
'*ayn*

ساق
saaq

ظَهر
zahr

يَد
yad

شَعر
sha'r

بَطن
baTn

أُذُن
U*THun*

أَنف
anf

فَم
fam

39

Someone has ripped up the Arabic words for parts of the body. Can you join the two halves of the word again?

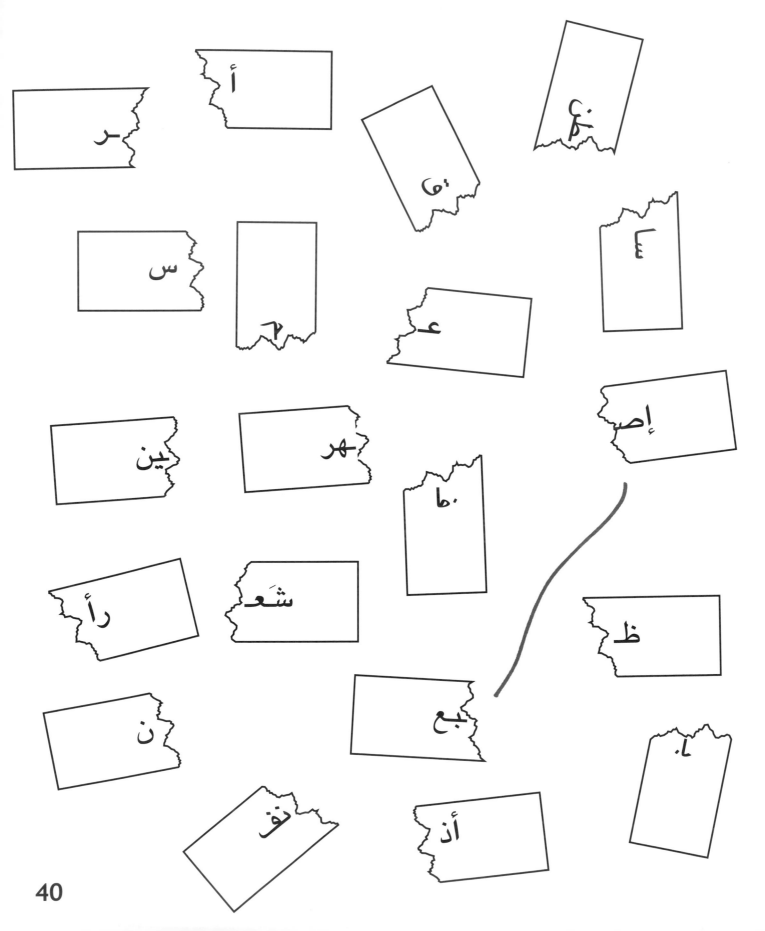

◎ **S**ee if you can find and circle six parts of the body in the word square, then draw them in the boxes below.

The words run *right to left*.

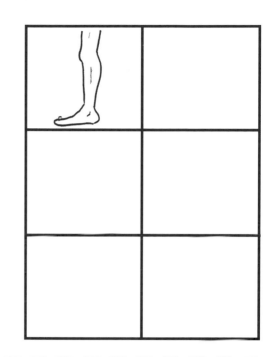

- -

◎ **N**ow match the Arabic to the pronunciation.

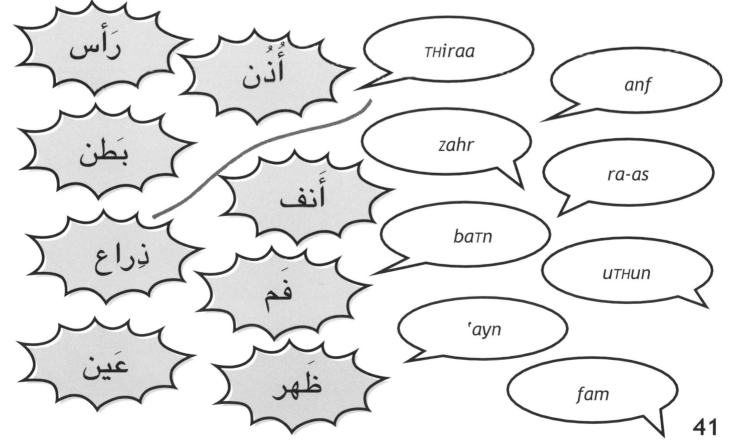

رَأْس

أُذُن

THiraa

anf

بَطن

zahr

ra-as

أَنف

baτn

uτʜun

ذِراع

فَم

'ayn

عَين

ظَهر

fam

41

Label the body with the correct number, and write the pronunciation next to the words.

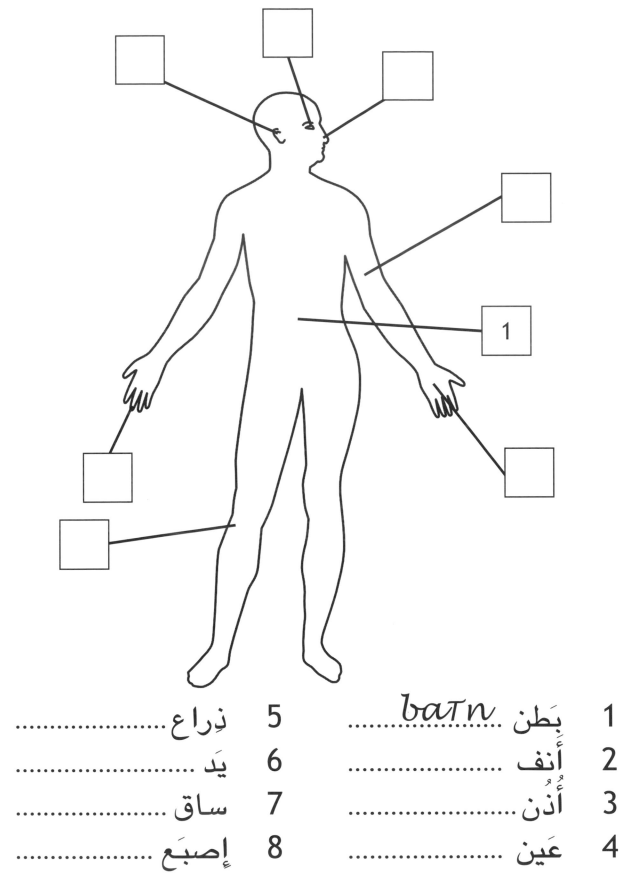

5	ذِراع	1	بَطن *baᴛn*
6	يَد	2	أنف ....
7	ساق	3	أُذُن ....
8	إِصبَع	4	عَين ....

◎ **F**inally, match the Arabic words, their pronunciation, and the English meanings, as in the example.

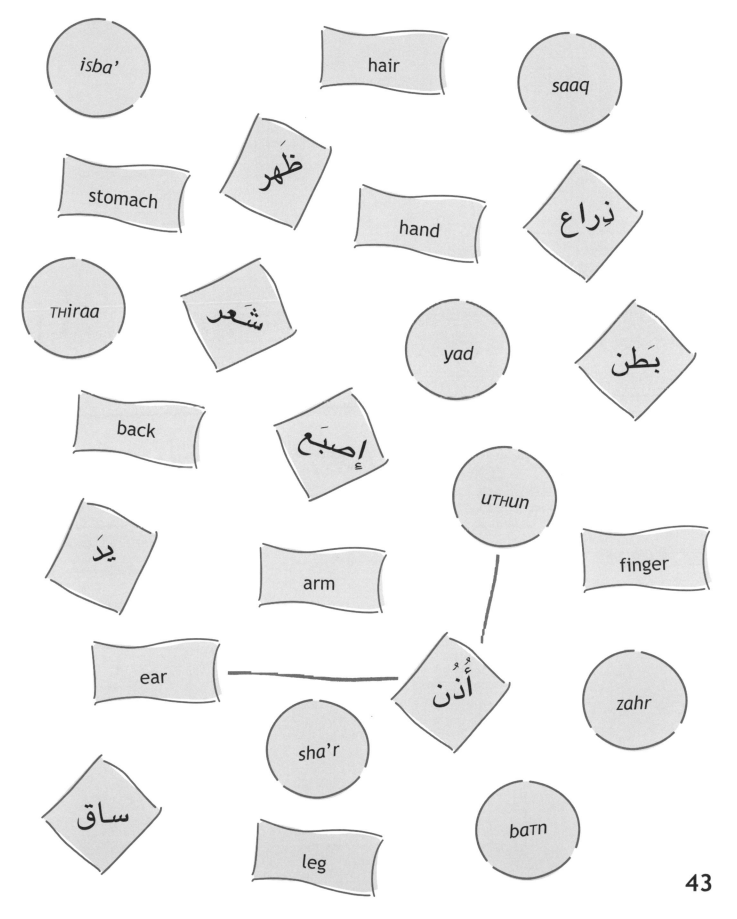

isba'

hair

saaq

ظَهر

stomach

hand

ذِراع

THiraa

شَعر

yad

بَطن

back

إصبَع

uTHun

يَد

finger

arm

ear

أُذُن

zahr

ساق

sha'r

baTn

leg

❽ USEFUL EXPRESSIONS

Look at the pictures.
Tear out the flashcards for this topic.
Follow steps 1 and 2 of the plan in the introduction.

أَين؟ *ayn?*

لا *laa*

نَعم *na'm*

مَع السَلامة *ma' as-salaama*

أَهلا *ahlan*

أَمس *ams*

اليَوم *al-yawm*

غَدا *ghadan*

هُنا *huna*

هُناك *hunaak*

الآن *al-aan*

بِكم؟ *bikam?*

آسِف *aasif*

عَظيم *'azeem*

مِن فَضلك *min faᴅlak*

شُكرا *shukran*

44

○ **M**atch the Arabic words to their English equivalents.

great   أَمس

yes   نَعم

yesterday   هُنا

where?   عَظيم

today

here   مِن فَضلك

please   لا

no   اليَوم

أَين؟

○ **N**ow match the Arabic to the pronunciation.

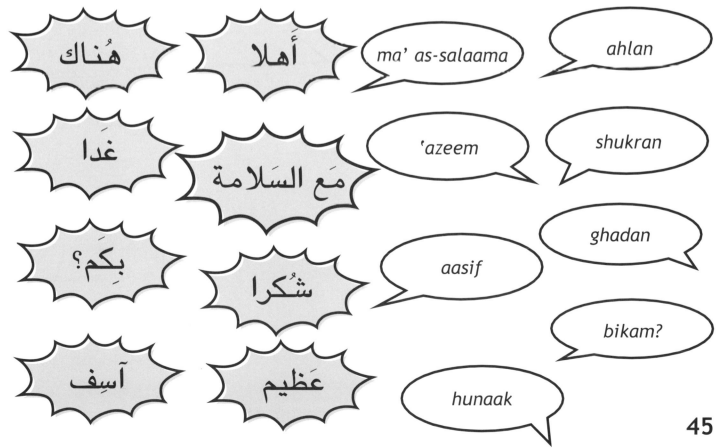

هُناك   أَهلا   *ma' as-salaama*   *ahlan*

غَدا   مَع السَلامة   *'azeem*   *shukran*

بِكَم؟   شُكرا   *aasif*   *ghadan*

bikam?

آسِف   عَظيم   *hunaak*

45

Choose the Arabic word that matches the picture to fill in the English word at the bottom of the page.

English word: (p) ( ) ( ) ( ) ( ) ( )

46

What are these people saying? Write the correct number in each speech bubble, as in the example.

7 أَينِ؟	5 هُنا	3 نَعم	1 أَهلا
8 بِكَم؟	6 آسِف	4 لا	2 مِن فَضلَك

◎ **F**inally, match the Arabic words, their pronunciation, and the English meanings, as in the example.

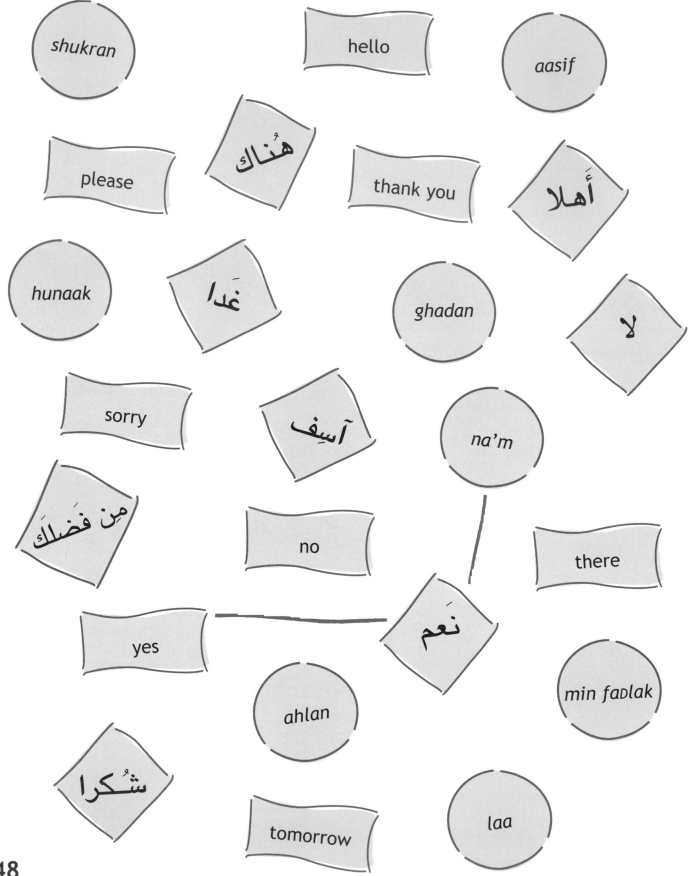

shukran

hello

aasif

please

هُناك

thank you

أَهلا

hunaak

غَدا

ghadan

لا

sorry

آسِف

na'm

مِن فَضلَك

no

there

yes

نَعم

min faDlak

ahlan

شُكرا

tomorrow

laa

48

This section is designed to review all the 100 words you have met in the different topics. It is a good idea to test yourself with your flashcards before trying this section.

These ten objects are hidden in the picture. Can you find and circle them?

كرسي   باب   قبعة   دراجة   سمكة

كلب   سرير   جورب   معطف   وردة

See if you can remember all these words.

اليوم

أوتوبيس

سريع

أنف

صحراء

نعم

دولاب

أسد

فستان

رخيص

نهر

ساق

50

Find the odd one out in these groups of words and say why.

قرد	مائدة	بقرة	كلب

Because it isn't an animal.

تليفون	قطار	اوتوبيس	سيارة

جيبة	قميص	معطف	مزرعة

شجرة	نهر	بحيرة	بحر

سينما	نظيف	وسخ	غالٍ

أسد	سمكة	قطة	أرنب

بطن	رأس	كنبة	ذراع

غدا	اليوم	أمس	من فضلك

ثلاجة	دولاب	سرير	فرن

◎ **L**ook at the objects below for 30 seconds.

◎ **C**over the picture and try to remember all the objects.
Circle the Arabic words for those you remember.

باب شكرا حذاء وردة

قطار معطف هنا لا سيارة

حصان كرسي جبل حزام

سرير عين تي شيرت جورب

قرد تليفزيون تاكسي شورت

Now match the Arabic words, their pronunciation, and the English meanings, as in the example.

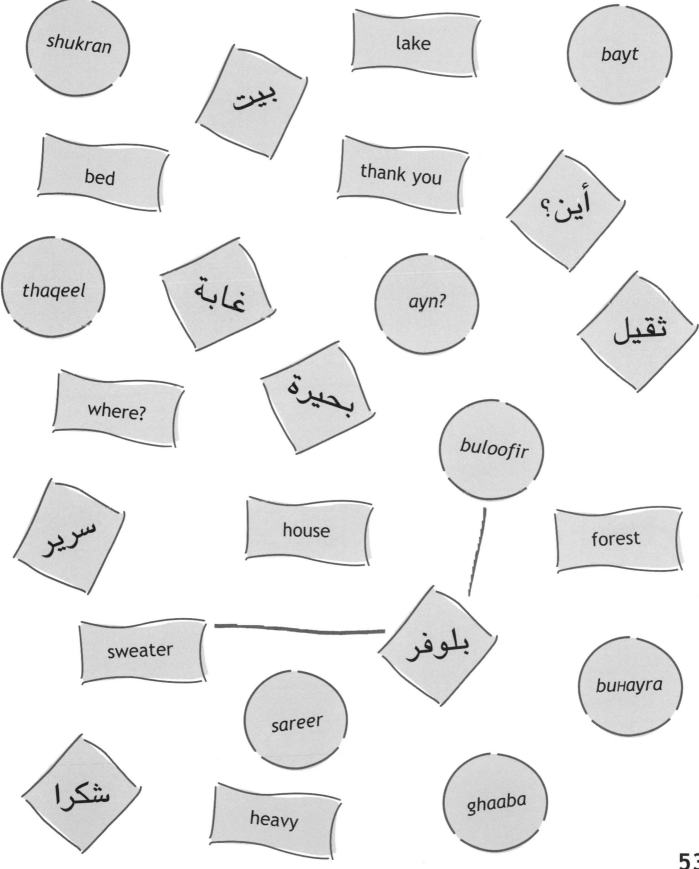

shukran

lake

bayt

بيت

bed

thank you

أين؟

thaqeel

غابة

ayn?

ثقيل

where?

بحيرة

buloofir

house

forest

سرير

sweater

بلوفر

buнayra

sareer

شكرا

heavy

ghaaba

Fill in the English phrase at the bottom of the page.

(w) كنبة	(g) تاكسي	(t) أذن	
(o) معطف	(a) وسخ	(e) جسر	
(m) نعم	(l) بكم؟	(i) اليوم	
(b) بقرة	(l) شباك	(h) مطعم	
(e) أين؟	(a) فم	(d) كلب	
(o) عين	(p) مائدة	(v) أهلا	
(n) تل	(y) لا	(r) اوتوبيس	
(n) أرنب	(e) شارع	(s) فرن	

English phrase: (w) ( ) ( ) ( )   ( ) ( ) ( ) ( ) !

Look at the two pictures and tick (✔) the objects that are different in Picture B.

 شورت

 تي شيرت

 باب

 قطة

Picture A

 كرسي

 سمكة

 جورب

 كلب

Picture B

Now join the Arabic words to their English equivalents.

English	Arabic
fridge	ذراع
trousers	بطن
shop	صغير
school	ثلاجة
river	محل
great	عظيم
small	نهر
light	بنطلون
arm	نظيف
stomach	خفيف
clean	حصان
horse	مدرسة

Try to match the Arabic to the pronunciation.

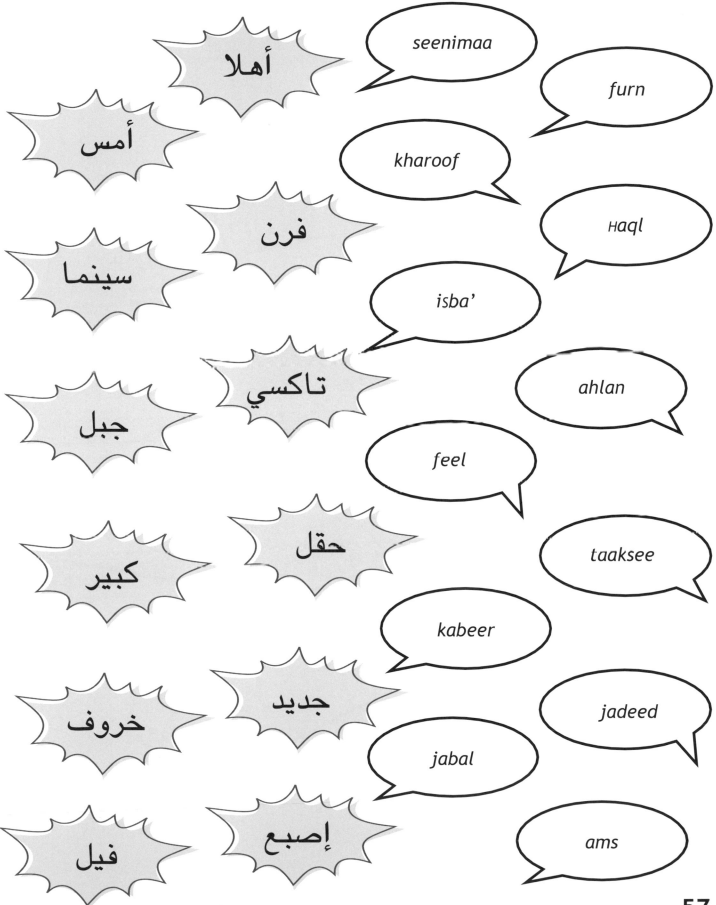

أهلا

أمس

سينما

فرن

جبل

تاكسي

كبير

حقل

خروف

جديد

فيل

إصبع

seenimaa

furn

kharoof

Haql

isba'

ahlan

feel

taaksee

kabeer

jadeed

jabal

ams

◎ Snake game.

● You will need a die and counter(s). You can challenge yourself to reach the finish or play with someone else. You have to throw the exact number to finish.

● Throw the die and move forward that number of spaces. When you land on a word you must pronounce it and say what it means in English. If you can't, you have to go back to the square you came from.

❶ AROUND THE HOME

Page 10 (top)

See page 9 for correct picture.

Page 10 (bottom)

door	باب
cupboard	دولاب
stove	فرن
bed	سرير
table	مائدة
chair	كرسي
fridge	ثلاجة
computer	كمبيوتر

Page 11 (top)

مائدة	*maa-ida*
دولاب	*doolaab*
كمبيوتر	*kumbiyootir*
سرير	*sareer*
شباك	*shubbaak*
تليفون	*tileefoon*
تليفزيون	*tileefizyoon*
كرسي	*kursee*

Page 11 (bottom)

Page 12

Page 13

English word: window

❷ CLOTHES

Page 15 (top)

فستان	*fustaan*
شورت	*shoort*
حذاء	*ΉiΤΉaa*
حزام	*Ήizaam*
قميص	*qamees*
تي شيرت	*tee-sheert*
قبعة	*qubba'a*
جورب	*jawrab*

Page 15 (bottom)

Page 16

hat	قبعة	*qubba'a*
shoe	حذاء	*ΉiΤΉaa*
sock	جورب	*jawrab*
shorts	شورت	*shoort*
t-shirt	تي شيرت	*tee-sheert*
belt	حزام	*Ήizaam*
coat	معطف	*mi'Taf*
trousers	بنطلون	*banTaloon*

Page 17

قبعة (hat)	2
معطف (coat)	0
حزام (belt)	2
حذاء (shoe)	2 (1 pair)
بنطلون (trousers)	0
شورت (shorts)	2
فستان (dress)	1
جورب (sock)	6 (3 pairs)
جيبة (skirt)	1
تي شيرت (t-shirt)	3
قميص (shirt)	0
بلوفر (sweater)	1

Page 18

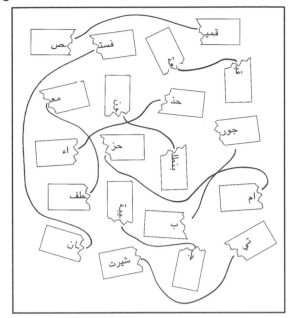

❸ AROUND TOWN

Page 20 (top)

cinema	سينما
shop	محل
hotel	فندق
taxi	تاكسي
car	سيارة
train	قطار
school	مدرسة
house	بيت

Page 20 (bottom)

bicycle	4
taxi	7
house	2
train	6
bus	1
road	3
car	5

Page 21

Page 22

English word: school

Page 23

اوتوبيس	*ootoobees*
تاكسي	*taaksee*
مدرسة	*madrasa*
سيارة	*sayyaara*
فندق	*funduq*
بيت	*bayt*
دراجة	*darraaja*
قطار	*qiтaar*
محل	*maнall*
سينما	*seenimaa*
مطعم	*maт'am*
شارع	*shaari'*

❹ COUNTRYSIDE

Page 25

See page 24 for correct picture.

Page 26

جسر	✔	حقل	✔
شجرة	✔	غابة	✘
صحراء	✘	بحيرة	✘
تل	✘	نهر	✔
جبل	✔	وردة	✔
بحر	✘	مزرعة	✔

Page 27 (top)

جبل	*jabal*
نهر	*nahr*
غابة	*ghaaba*
صحراء	*saнraa*
بحر	*baнr*
مزرعة	*mazra'a*
جسر	*jisr*
حقل	*наql*

Page 27 (bottom)

ه	و	س	ب	ث	ي	ن	ـنـ	ـفـ
ة	ر	ـجـ	ـشـ	خ	و	ـجـ	ر	ر
د	ه	ـتـ	د	ر	و	ث	ـد	ر
ة	ـيـ	ـحـ	ـبـ	د	ق	و	ظ	ر
ق	ـعـ	ي	ر	ز	م	ث	ـهـ	ر
ف	ي	ن	و	ـبـ	ظ	ـل	ـتـ	
م	و	ـط	ـقـ	ـمـ	ف	و	غ	
ب	ـمـ	ذ	ا	ـر	ـسـ	ـجـ	ض	

Page 28

sea	بحر	*baнr*
lake	بحيرة	*buнayra*
desert	صحراء	*saнraa*
farm	مزرعة	*mazra'a*
flower	وردة	*warda*
mountain	جبل	*jabal*
river	نهر	*nahrr*
field	حقل	*наql*

❺ OPPOSITES

Page 30

expensive	غـال
big	كبير
light	خفيف
slow	بطىء
clean	نظيف
inexpensive	رخيص
dirty	وسخ
small	صغير
heavy	ثقيل
new	جديد
fast	سريع
old	قديم

Page 31

English word: change

Page 32

Odd one outs are those which are not opposites:

ثقيل

صغير

جديد

وسخ

بطىء

رخيص

Page 33

old	جديد
big	صغير
new	قديم
slow	سريع
dirty	نظيف
small	كبير
heavy	خفيف
clean	وسخ
light	ثقيل
expensive	رخيص
inexpensive	غال

❻ ANIMALS

Page 35

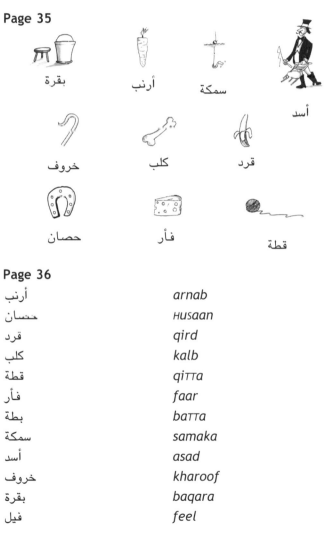

بقرة   أرنب   سمكة   أسد

خروف   كلب   قرد

حصان   فأر   قطة

Page 36

أرنب	*arnab*
حصان	*нusaan*
قرد	*qird*
كلب	*kalb*
قطة	*qiтта*
فأر	*faar*
بطة	*baтта*
سمكة	*samaka*
أسد	*asad*
خروف	*kharoof*
بقرة	*baqara*
فيل	*feel*

Page 37

elephant	✔	mouse	✘
monkey	✘	cat	✔
sheep	✔	dog	✘
lion	✔	cow	✔
fish	✔	horse	✘
duck	✘	rabbit	✔

Page 38

monkey	قرد
cow	بقرة
mouse	فأر
dog	كلب
sheep	خروف
fish	سمكة
lion	أسد
elephant	فيل
cat	قطة
duck	بطة
rabbit	أرنب
horse	حصان

❼ PARTS OF THE BODY

Page 40

Page 41 (top)

You should have also drawn pictures of:
leg; mouth; ear; nose; eye; hair

62

Page 41 (bottom)

رأس	ra-as
أذن	uтнun
بطن	baтn
أنف	anf
ذراع	тнiraa
فم	fam
عين	'ayn
ظهر	zahr

Page 42

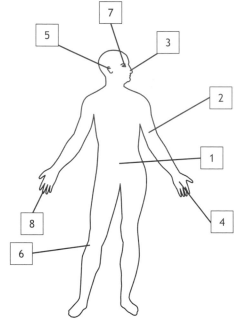

1.	بطن	baтn
2.	ذراع	тнiraa
3.	أنف	anf
4.	يد	yad
5.	أذن	uтнun
6.	ساق	saaq
7.	عين	'ayn
8.	أصبع	isba'

Page 43

ear	أذن	uтнun
hair	شعر	sha'r
hand	يد	yad
stomach	بطن	baтn
arm	ذراع	тнiraa
back	ظهر	zahr
finger	أصبع	isba'
leg	ساق	saaq

8 USEFUL EXPRESSIONS

Page 45 (top)

great	عظيم
yes	نعم
yesterday	أمس
where?	أين؟
today	اليوم
here	هنا
please	من فضلك
no	لا

Page 45 (bottom)

هناك	*hunaak*
أهلا	*ahlan*
غدا	*ghadan*
مع السلامة	*ma' as-salaama*
بكم؟	*bikam?*
شكرا	*shukran*
آسف	*aasif*
عظيم	*'azeem*

Page 46

English word: please

Page 47

Page 48

yes	نعم	*na'm*
hello	أهلا	*ahlan*
no	لا	*laa*
sorry	آسف	*aasif*
please	من فضلك	*min faɒlak*
there	هناك	*hunaak*
thank you	شكرا	*shukran*
tomorrow	غدا	*ghadan*

● ROUND-UP

Page 49

Page 50

صحراء =

أسد =

نعم =

دولاب =

رخيص =

اليوم =

نهر =

أنف =

فستان =

ساق =

سريع =

أتوبيس =

Page 51

مائدة (Because it isn't an animal.)

تليفون (Because it isn't a means of transportation.)

مزرعة (Because it isn't an item of clothing.)

شجرة (Because it isn't connected with water.)

سينما (Because it isn't a descriptive word.)

سمكة (Because it lives in water/doesn't have legs.)

كنبة (Because it isn't a part of the body.)

من فضلك (Because it isn't an expression of time.)

سرير (Because you wouldn't find it in the kitchen.)

63

Page 52

Words that appear in the picture:

تي شيرت

سيارة

وردة

حذاء

قطار

قرد

تليفزيون

كرسي

حزام

شورت

Page 53

sweater	بلوفر	*buloofir*
lake	بحيرة	*buнayra*
thank you	شكرا	*shukran*
bed	سرير	*sareer*
house	بيت	*bayt*
forest	غابة	*ghaaba*
where?	أين؟	*ayn*
heavy	ثقيل	*thaqeel*

Page 54

English phrase: well done!

Page 55

شورت	✔ (shade)
تي شيرت	✗
باب	✔ (handle)
قطة	✗
كرسي	✔ (back)
سمكة	✔ (direction)
جورب	✔ (pattern)
كلب	✗

Page 56

fridge	ثلاجة
trousers	بنطلون
shop	محل
school	مدرسة
river	نهر
great	عظيم
small	صغير
light	خفيف
arm	ذراع
stomach	بطن
clean	نظيف
horse	حصان

Page 57

أهلا	*ahlan*
أمس	*ams*
فرن	*furn*
سينما	*seenimaa*
تاكسي	*taaksee*
جبل	*jabal*
حقل	*наql*
كبير	*kabeer*
جديد	*jadeed*
خروف	*kharoof*
إصبع	*isba'*
فيل	*feel*

Page 58

Here are the English equivalents and pronunciation of the words, in order from START to FINISH:

head *ra-as*	farm *mazra'a*	duck *baтta*
cow *baqara*	old *qadeem*	dirty *wasikh*
hotel *funduq*	rabbit *arnab*	hand *yad*
sea *baнr*	slow *baтee*	heavy *thaqeel*
no *laa*	ear *uтнun*	tomorrow *ghadan*
there *hunaak*	expensive *ghalee*	back *zahr*
table *maa-ida*	hair *sha'r*	leg *saaq*
now *al-aan*	chair *kursee*	yes *na'm*

كمبيوتر

kumbiyootir

شباك

shubbaak

مائدة

maa-ida

دولاب

doolaab

ثلاجة

thallaaja

كرسي

kursee

كنبة

kanaba

فرن

furn

باب

baab

سرير

sareer

تليفون

tileefoon

تليفزيون

tileefizyoon

window	computer
cupboard	table
chair	fridge
stove	sofa
bed	door
television	telephone

حزام

HIzaam

معطف

mi'Taf

جيبة

jeeba

قبعة

qubba'a

تي شيرت

tee-sheert

حذاء

HITHaa

بلوفر

buloofir

قميص

qamees

شورت

shoort

جورب

jawrab

بنطلون

banTaloon

فستان

fustaan

coat	belt
hat	skirt
shoe	t-shirt
shirt	sweater
sock	shorts
dress	trousers

سيارة *sayyaara*	مدرسة *madrasa*
سينما *seenimaa*	شارع *shaari'*
محل *maHall*	فندق *funduq*
دراجة *darraaja*	تاكسي *taaksee*
أوتوبيس *ootoobees*	مطعم *maT'am*
بيت *bayt*	قطار *qiTaar*

car	school
cinema	road
shop	hotel
bicycle	taxi
bus	restaurant
house	train

غابة	بحيرة
ghaaba	*buнayra*

بحر	تل
baнr	*tal*

شجرة	جبل
shajara	*jabal*

وردة	صحراء
warda	*saнraa*

نهر	جسر
nahr	*jisr*

حقل	مزرعة
наql	*mazra'a*

forest	lake
sea	hill
tree	mountain
flower	desert
river	bridge
field	farm

ثقيل

thaqeel

خفيف

khafeef

كبير

kabeer

صغير

sagheer

قديم

qadeem

جديد

jadeed

سريع

saree'

بطيء

baтee

نظيف

nazeef

وسخ

wasikh

رخيص

rakhees

غالٍ

ghaalee

light	heavy
small	big
new	old
slow	fast
dirty	clean
expensive	cheap

قطة qiττa	بطة baττa
بقرة baqara	فأر faar
كلب kalb	أرنب arnab
قرد qird	حصان ниsaan
سمكة samaka	أسد asad
خروف kharoof	فيل feel

cat	duck
cow	mouse
dog	rabbit
monkey	horse
fish	lion
sheep	elephant

٧

إصبع *isba'*	ذراع *THiraa'*
فم *fam*	رأس *ra-as*
ساق *saaq*	أذن *uTHun*
بطن *baTn*	يد *yad*
شعر *sha'r*	عين *'ayn*
ظهر *zahr*	أنف *anf*

finger	arm
mouth	head
leg	ear
stomach	hand
hair	eye
back	nose

شكرا *shukran*	من فضلك *min faɒlak*
لا *laa*	نعم *na'm*
مع السلامة *ma' as-salaama*	أهلا *ahlan*
اليوم *al-yaum*	أمس *ams*
أين؟ *ayn*	غداً *ghadan*
هناك *hunaak*	هنا *huna*
بكم؟ *bikam*	آسف *aasif*
الآن *al-aan*	عظيم! *'azeem*

thank you	please
no	yes
goodbye	hello
today	yesterday
where?	tomorrow
there	here
how much?	sorry!
now	great!